animate
FAITH

ILLUSTRATED BY
PAUL SOUPISET

WRITTEN BY
CARLA BARNHILL
& TONY JONES

SPARK
HOUSE
wearesparkhouse.org

MINNEAPOLIS, MN

CONTRIBUTORS
NADIA BOLZ-WEBER, LILLIAN DANIEL,
SHANE HIPPS, BRAIN MCLAREN,
BRUCE REYES-CHOW, MARK SCANDRETTE,
LAUREN WINNER

JOURNAL ILLUSTRATION
PAUL SOUPISET, WITH ADDITIONAL
ILLUSTRATION BY MARK GUTIERREZ,
FOR TOOLBOX STUDIOS, INC.

JOURNAL WRITERS
CARLA BARNHILL, TONY JONES

SPARKHOUSE TEAM
ANDREW DEYOUNG, SUE HINTON,
TONY JONES, JIM KAST-KEAT, TIMOTHY
PAULSON, DAVID SCHOENKNECHT,
KRISTOFER SKRADE

TOOLBOX STUDIOS TEAM
PAUL SOUPISET, MARK GUTIERREZ,
BRET REPKA, STACY THOMAS,
GABRIEL PARDO

VIDEO TEAM
KYLE ISENHOWER OF ISENHOWER
PRODUCTIONS, SHANE NELSON OF
OMNI-FUSION MEDIA PRODUCTION,
SILAS KINDY OF ONE LIGHT COLLECTIVE

EDITORIAL TEAM
ERIN DAVIS

SPECIAL THANKS TO PHOTOGRAPHER
COURTNEY PERRY

THE PAPER USED IN THIS PUBLICATION
MEETS THE MINIMUM REQUIREMENTS
OF AMERICAN NATIONAL STANDARD FOR
INFORMATION SCIENCES — PERMANENCE OF
PAPER FOR PRINTED LIBRARY MATERIALS,
ANSI Z329 . 48 -1984

MANUFACTURED IN THE U.S.A.

16 15 14 13 12   2 3 4 5 6 7 8 9 10

ISBN 978-1-4514-3084-4

 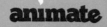

animate

FAITH

GOD | FAITH IS A QUEST
BRIAN MCLAREN | 7

RELIGION | SPIRITUALITY IS NOT ENOUGH
LILLIAN DANIEL | 23

JESUS | THE REVOLUTION OF LOVE
MARK SCANDRETTE | 39

SALVATION | ABUNDANT LIFE NOW
SHANE HIPPS | 55

CROSS | WHERE GOD IS
NADIA BOLZ-WEBER | 71

BIBLE | A BOOK LIKE NO OTHER
LAUREN WINNER | 87

CHURCH | AN IMPERFECT FAMILY
BRUCE REYES-CHOW | 103

THIS JOURNAL IS PRETTY AMAZING TO LOOK AT.
IT'S GOT GORGEOUS ILLUSTRATIONS CREATED
BY PHENOMENALLY TALENTED ARTISTS AND
THOUGHT-PROVOKING WORDS FROM SOME OF
THE MOST INNOVATIVE CHRISTIAN THINKERS AND
PRACTITIONERS IN THE COUNTRY.

BUT IT'S NOT DONE, NOT BY A LONG SHOT.

THE PAGES OF THIS JOURNAL AREN'T MEANT TO
SIT THERE AND LOOK PRETTY. THEY ARE INTENDED
TO BE A SPRINGBOARD FOR YOUR IMAGES, YOUR
WORDS, YOUR PHENOMENAL CREATIONS AND
THOUGH-PROVOKING IDEAS. SO SCRIBBLE ON THE
PAGES, WRITE DOWN YOUR THOUGHTS, COLOR
OUTSIDE OF THE LINES—SERIOUSLY. MAKE THIS
THING YOUR OWN. NO ONE IS GOING TO LOOK OVER
YOUR SHOULDER TO CHECK YOUR WORK. NO ONE
IS HANDING OUT GOLD STARS TO THE STUDENT
WHO GETS THE RIGHT ANSWERS. REALLY, NO ONE
IS CONVINCED THERE IS ONLY ONE RIGHT ANSWER.

THE ANIMATE SERIES IS DESIGNED TO BE A UNIQUE
WAY OF DIGGING INTO SOME OF THE QUESTIONS
WE ALL HAVE ABOUT FAITH AND SPIRITUALITY:

- IS GOD REAL?
- CAN WE BE SPIRITUAL WITHOUT BEING RELIGIOUS?
- WHAT IS SALVATION?
- WHY READ THE BIBLE?
- WHAT WAS JESUS UP TO?
- WHAT REALLY HAPPENED ON THE CROSS?
- WHAT DOES IT MEAN TO BE THE CHURCH?

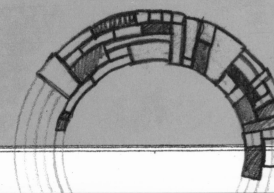

MAYBE YOU'VE BEEN ASKING THESE QUESTIONS FOR A WHILE. MAYBE YOU'VE NEVER REALLY THOUGHT MUCH ABOUT THEM. MAYBE YOU'RE SICK OF YOUR FRIENDS BAD-MOUTHING RELIGION. WHATEVER YOUR EXPERIENCE IS, YOU ARE INVITED TO JOIN IN A KIND OF EXPEDITION WHERE THE ROUTE IS A LITTLE UNCHARTED AND THE TERRITORY A BIT MYSTERIOUS.

IF THAT FEELS UNSETTLING TO YOU, DON'T WORRY. YOUR FELLOW TRAVELERS ARE PEOPLE WHO'VE BEEN WALKING THIS PATH FOR A WHILE—PEOPLE LIKE BRIAN MCLAREN AND NADIA BOLZ-WEBER AND BRUCE REYES-CHOW AND LAUREN WINNER. EACH OF THEM IS FAR MORE INTERESTED IN ASKING QUESTIONS THAN ANSWERING THEM. SO FEEL FREE TO DO THE SAME.

AS YOU WORK THROUGH EACH SESSION, IF SOMETHING STRIKES YOU AS WORTH TALKING ABOUT, TALK ABOUT IT. IF SOMETHING ELSE FEELS UNINSPIRING, GO AHEAD AND SKIP THAT PART. THIS IS YOUR JOURNEY AND YOU GET TO DECIDE WHEN TO STOP AND LINGER AND WHEN TO KEEP MOVING.

ALONG THE WAY, YOU'LL BE KEEPING THIS JOURNAL, CREATING A KIND OF KEEPSAKE OF YOUR TRAVELS. DURING THE GROUP SESSIONS, YOUR FACILITATOR WILL OFFER SUGGESTIONS FOR ACTIVITIES AND DEEPER DISCUSSION. BUT IN THE DAYS BETWEEN SESSIONS, YOU'RE ENCOURAGED TO REVISIT THOSE IDEAS THAT ARE COMPELLING TO YOU AND DIG A LITTLE MORE. ADD AN ILLUSTRATION, WRITE DOWN A QUESTION, SKETCH OUT AN IDEA, CRAFT A BETTER METAPHOR.

Make it your own

animate ⟨

GOD | FAITH IS A QUEST
BRIAN MCLAREN

WHO IS Brian McLAREN

BRIAN MCLAREN GRABBED THE ATTENTION OF DISENCHANTED CHRISTIANS WITH HIS BOOK *A NEW KIND OF CHRISTIAN* (2001). LATER, IN 2005, HE WAS NAMED ONE OF TIME MAGAZINE'S 25 MOST INFLUENTIAL EVANGELICALS IN AMERICA. BRIAN'S INFLUENCE HAS BEEN THE RESULT OF HIS WILLINGNESS TO ADMIT THAT HE ISN'T ALWAYS SURE ABOUT HIS FAITH AND THAT HE USUALLY HAS FAR MORE QUESTIONS THAN ANSWERS.

MORE BRIAN TRIVIA:

+ BRIAN WAS A COLLEGE ENGLISH PROFESSOR WHEN HE AND HIS WIFE STARTED A CHURCH IN THEIR LIVING ROOM.
+ THAT CHURCH BECAME CEDAR RIDGE COMMUNITY CHURCH AND BRIAN WAS THEIR PASTOR FOR NEARLY 20 YEARS.
+ LIVES ON MARCO ISLAND IN FLORIDA WHERE HE RAISES DOZENS OF EXOTIC TORTOISES IN HIS BACKYARD
+ RELEASED AN ALBUM OF ORIGINAL MUSIC CALLED "LEARNING HOW TO LOVE" IN 1978.
+ BA AND MA IN ENGLISH FROM UNIVERSITY OF MARYLAND

BRIAN'S BOOKS:

+ A NEW KIND OF CHRISTIAN
+ A GENEROUS ORTHODOXY
+ EVERYTHING MUST CHANGE
+ NAKED SPIRITUALITY

12 GAUGE NAILS

"Sometimes, when I hear people speak about God, I feel like an atheist. The God they speak of I don't believe in: a God who loves Christians but hates Muslims; or a God who pours luxuries on the rich but consigns the poor to poverty; or a God who cares about human souls but doesn't care about conserving and protecting our beautiful, fragile planet. So if you ask me, "Is God real?" I first have to ask, "Which God are we talking about? And what do you mean by God?""

—Brian McLaren

CONFESSION

WHAT IMAGES OF GOD HAVE YOU LET GO OF?

WHAT IMAGES OF GOD RESONATE WITH YOU?

"IN OUR EFFORTS TO MAKE SENSE OF GOD,
BRIAN SUGGESTS THAT WE HAVE PUSHED
OURSELVES ONTO TWO ISLANDS:

ON ONE, WE GATHER AROUND AN IMAGE OF GOD
AS A FORTRESS, OUR STRENGTH AND SHIELD.
GOD IS OUR ROCK—SOLID, UNCHANGING, STEADY.

ON THE OTHER, WE FIND OURSELVES HOVERING
AROUND A FLOATING CASTLE ON A CLOUD, WHERE GOD
IS FOGGY AND SPECULATIVE. GOD IS EVERYWHERE
AND NOWHERE. GOD IS UNKNOWABLE, MYSTICAL,
AND FAR OUTSIDE OF HUMAN EXPERIENCE."

CERTITUDE

THE TRINITY IS A GREAT EXAMPLE OF HOW
COMPLICATED IT CAN BE TO ANSWER THE QUESTION
"WHO IS GOD?"

THE DOCTRINE OF THE TRINITY ISN'T REALLY IN THE
BIBLE—THERE WE FIND THE SEEDS OF THIS IDEA. BUT
EARLY CHRISTIANS NEEDED WAYS TO TALK ABOUT
GOD BEING THE BABY IN THE MANGER, THE BREATH
OF LIFE, AND THE CREATOR OF THE UNIVERSE.

BY THE 5TH CENTURY, WE HAD A DOCTRINE OF THE
TRINITY, BUT IT'S A CONCEPT MANY OF US STILL HAVE
A HARD TIME UNDERSTANDING.

ἀπόφασις

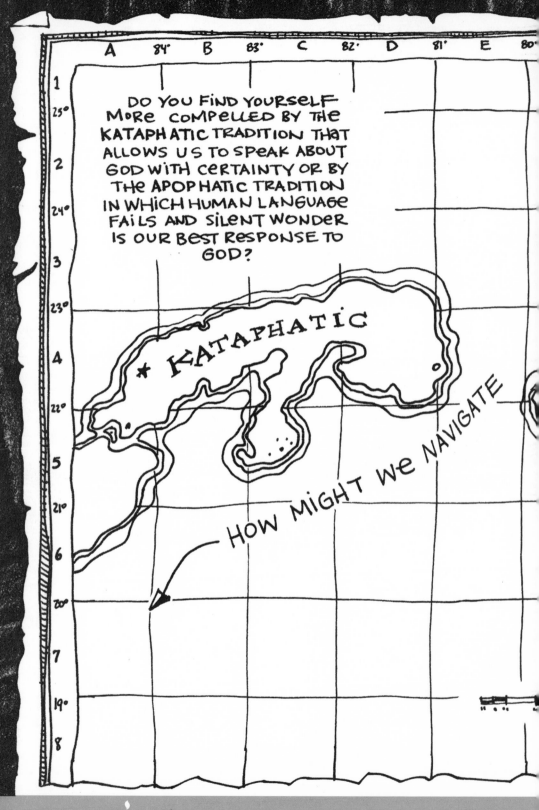

We are

animate

EMBARKED.

GOD IS THE WIND IN THE SAIL AND THE SEA WE SAIL UPON; THE SOURCE AND GOAL OF OUR QUEST. HOW ARE YOU EMBARKED ON A journey OF SEEKING GOD AND KEEPING THE QUEST ALIVE?

NOTES

~~~~~~~~~~~~~~~~NOTES

animate

RELIGION | SPRITUALITY IS NOT ENOUGH
LILLIAN DANIEL

Reclaiming Religion

FOR LILLIAN DANIEL, FAITH ISN'T SOMETHING WE MAKE FOR OURSELVES. IT'S A LONG, HARDY TRADITION THAT WE ENTER AND ADD TO. SHE PUSHES BACK AT THE IDEA THAT IT'S POSSIBLE TO BE "SPIRITUAL" WITHOUT BEING "RELIGIOUS."

FOR MANY PEOPLE TODAY, THIS QUESTION OF WHAT IT MEANS TO BE A PERSON OF FAITH HAS BECOME A STICKING POINT. IT KEEPS SOME PEOPLE AWAY FROM THE CHURCH. IT KEEPS OTHERS CLINGING TO TRADITIONS THAT MAY HAVE LOST THEIR MEANING. SO WHAT SHOULD WE MAKE OF THIS OFTEN MUDDY, WEEDY GARDEN OF RELIGION THAT WE FIND OURSELVES IN?

LILLIAN'S BOOKS:

+ TELL IT LIKE IT IS: RECLAIMING THE PRACTICE OF TESTIMONY
+ THIS ODD AND WONDROUS CALLING: THE PUBLIC AND PRIVATE LIVES OF TWO MINISTERS

MORE LILLIAN TRIVIA:

+ SENIOR MINISTER OF FIRST CONGREGATIONAL CHURCH IN GLEN ELLYN, ILLINOIS
+ CO-HOSTS A WEEKLY TV PROGRAM IN CHICAGO CALLED 30 GOOD MINUTES
+ FREQUENT CONTRIBUTOR TO CHRISTIAN CENTURY MAGAZINE AND THE HUFFINGTON POST
+ WON THE DISTINGUISHED ALUMNI AWARD AT YALE DIV. SCHOOL

+ MDIV. FROM YALE UNIVERSITY DIVINITY SCHOOL

GREEN-GRO SEEDS

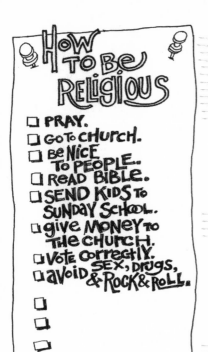

HOW TO BE RELIGIOUS

- ☐ PRAY.
- ☐ GO TO CHURCH.
- ☐ BE NICE TO PEOPLE.
- ☐ READ BIBLE.
- ☐ SEND KIDS TO SUNDAY SCHOOL.
- ☐ GIVE MONEY TO THE CHURCH.
- ☐ VOTE CORRECTLY.
- ☐ AVOID SEX, DRUGS, & ROCK & ROLL.
- ☐
- ☐
- ☐

LILLIAN SUGGESTS THAT IT'S A GOOD THING TO BE PART OF SOMETHING BIGGER THAN OURSELVES. HOW DOES THAT IDEA SIT WITH YOU WHEN IT COMES TO RELIGION?

DO YOU THINK OF YOURSELF AS A RELIGIOUS PERSON?

WHAT DOES THAT MEAN TO YOU? ADD YOUR THOUGHTS TO THE CHECKLIST.

I think, THAT WHEN we **invent** OUR OWN SPIRITUALITY, WITH A *flower* FROM Here AND ANOTHER FROM THERE, it's a bouquet that DOESN'T live LONG. Religious TRADITIONS CREATED OVER TIME, AND, THANK GOD BY PEOPLE WHO ARE NOT ME, THOSE HAVE A LONGER SHELF LIFE. THE beauty OF A LONG TRADITION IS THAT IT IS BIGGER THAN anything WE COULD DO BY OURSELVES.

Lillian Daniel

Spiritual but and not Religious

SPiRiTUAL peoPLe

(VENNCREDIBLE)

...BOTH...

ACCORDING TO MOST
RESEARCH, NEARLY
90% OF THE PEOPLE
ON THE PLANET
BELIEVE IN A DIVINE
BEING AND MAKE
SENSE OF THIS
BELIEF THROUGH
SOME KIND OF
ORGANIZED RELIGION.
SO WHY DO PEOPLE
TEND TO REJECT
"ORGANIZED RELIGION"?

WHAT WOULD IT
LOOK LIKE TO BE
SPIRITUAL WITHOUT
BEING RELIGIOUS?

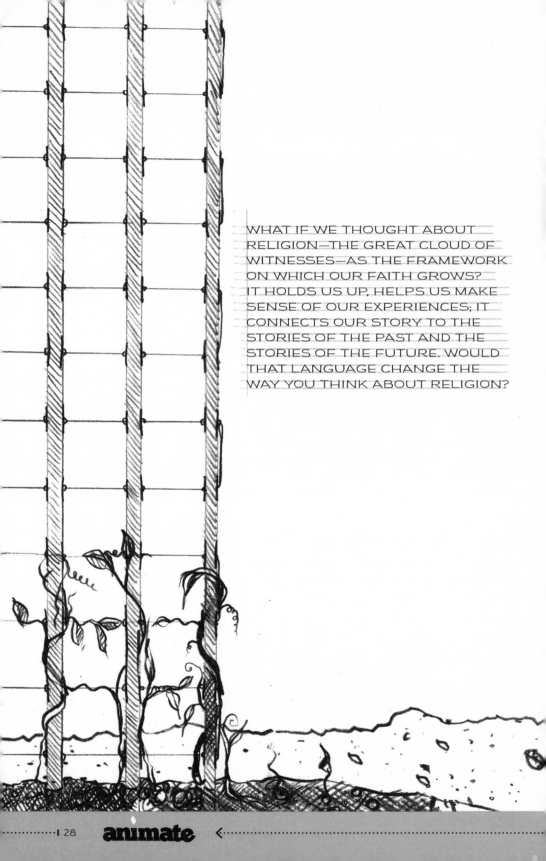

WHAT IF WE THOUGHT ABOUT RELIGION—THE GREAT CLOUD OF WITNESSES—AS THE FRAMEWORK ON WHICH OUR FAITH GROWS? IT HOLDS US UP, HELPS US MAKE SENSE OF OUR EXPERIENCES; IT CONNECTS OUR STORY TO THE STORIES OF THE PAST AND THE STORIES OF THE FUTURE. WOULD THAT LANGUAGE CHANGE THE WAY YOU THINK ABOUT RELIGION?

Building a Framework

" Since we are surrounded by so great a cloud of witnesses, let us also lay aside every weight and the sin that clings so closely, and let us run with perseverance the race that is set before us..." HEBREWS 12:1

WHAT CAN WE DO WITH THOSE PLACES IN THE GARDEN THAT ARE UGLY OR DANGEROUS OR UNPLEASANT?

DOES THE BEAUTY OF THE TRADITION OVERSHADOW THE UGLINESS?

ADD SOME "PLANTS" TO YOUR GARDEN— THE YOGA RETREAT, YOUR GRANDPA'S JUDAISM, SOME WEIRD BOOK THAT'S SPIRITUAL BUT NOT RELIGIOUS—THINGS THAT HAVE SHAPED YOUR RELIGIOUS EXPERIENCE.

Seeding the Soil

WHAT'S BEEN VALUABLE IN
YOUR TRADITION?

WHAT HAVE YOU GATHERED FROM
OTHER TRADITIONS THAT HAS MADE
YOUR FAITH MORE MEANINGFUL?

LILLIAN FOUND HER PLACE IN "A GARDEN BIGGER THAN MY OWN." HAVE YOU FOUND YOUR PLACE?

...ming

IF NOT, WHAT KIND OF
PRUNING OR FERTILIZER
DO YOU NEED TO
PUT DOWN ROOTS
AND BLOOM IN THE
CHRISTIAN TRADITION?

NOTES

NOTES

animate

JESUS | THE REVOLUTION OF LOVE
MARK SCANDRETTE

MARK AND HIS FAMILY MOVED TO SAN FRANCISCO IN 2000 TO PLANT A CHURCH. BUT THE MORE MARK GOT INTO LIFE AS A PASTOR, THE MORE HE FELT LIKE THE SO-CALLED "TRADITIONAL" MODELS OF CHURCH WEREN'T WORKING. INSTEAD, HE FOUND HIMSELF DRAWN TOWARD THIS IDEA OF THE CHURCH AS A PLACE WHERE PEOPLE WOULD BECOME APPRENTICES OF JESUS; THE JESUS DOJO.

THE RESULT IS REIMAGINE, A COLLECTIVE THAT INVITES PEOPLE INTO INTEGRATIVE SPIRITUAL EXPERIMENTS AND PRACTICES, WITH AN EMPHASIS ON CREATIVITY, COMMUNITY BUILDING, AND SOCIAL ACTION.

WHO IS Mark SCANDRETTE

"WE LONG FOR REST AND PEACE IN OUR LIVES AND FOR HEALING IN OUR WORLD. JESUS PROMISES THAT BY LEARNING TO FOLLOW HIS WAY, WE WILL EXPERIENCE THAT REST AND BECOME AGENTS OF GOD'S HEALING IN OUR WORLD."

MORE MARK TRIVIA

+ ROASTS HIS OWN COFFEE IN A CAST IRON SKILLET EVERY MORNING

+ CONCEIVED IN SPAIN, BORN IN GERMANY, GREW UP IN MINNESOTA, AND NOW CALLS SAN FRANCISCO HOME

+ WAS A CHILD EVANGELIST

+ HAS NEVER TAKEN A KARATE CLASS

+ BA IN APPLIED PSYCH FROM BEMIDJI STATE

+ STUDIED FOR MDIV AT BETHEL THEOLOGICAL SEMINARY

MARK'S BOOKS:

+ PRACTICING THE WAY OF JESUS

+ SOUL GRAFFITI

RISKY BUSINESS

LAZARUS, COME FORTH!

JESUS SAID AND DID PLENTY OF STRANGE THINGS IN HIS LIFE. WHICH STORIES STICK WITH YOU?

WHAT WAS @ STAKE FOR JESUS WHEN HE DID THOSE THINGS?

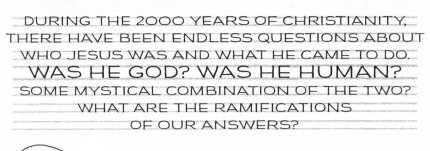

WHO DO I NEED TO FORGIVE?

WHO ARE THE ENEMIES THAT I'M CALLED TO **LOVE** AND BLESS?

WHO IS THE **WOUNDED** PERSON THAT I'VE WALKED PAST?

WHO IS "SICK AND IN PRISON" IN **MY** LIFE?

COFFEE + SANDWICHES

THE MASTER
IS IN THE
DOJO.
WHAT IS ONE NEW PRACTICE YOU CAN LEARN FROM HIM?

NOTES

NOTES

animate

SALVATION | ABUNDANT LIFE NOW
SHANE HIPPS

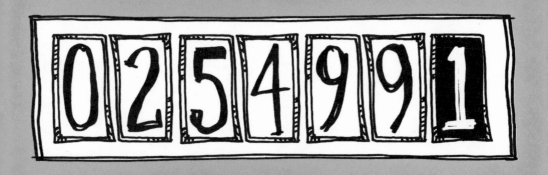

What is Salvation?

SHANE USES SOME VIVID IMAGES TO SUGGEST SALVATION—THE UNCOILING ROPE, THE EYE OF THE HURRICANE, THE MAIN COURSE OF THE FEAST. HOW WOULD YOU DESCRIBE THE MOMENTS OF SALVATION IN YOUR LIFE?

WHAT DO THOSE MOMENTS SUGGEST ABOUT WHAT MIGHT BE WAITING FOR US AFTER DEATH?

YOU WILL BE SAVED; YOU AND YOUR HOUSEHOLD.

cheque €477,-

SHANE HIPPS CAME TO MINISTRY FROM THE WORLD OF HIGH-END ADVERTISING. SO IT'S NOT SURPRISING THAT HE HAS A KNACK FOR UNPACKING THE DEEPER LAYERS OF THE GOSPEL MESSAGE. FOR SHANE, THERE IS MORE TO OUR IDEAS ABOUT SALVATION THAN JUST WHAT HAPPENS AFTER WE DIE. HE SAYS, "SALVATION IS NOT JUST A ONE-TIME PROMISE FOR WHEN WE DIE. IT'S A MOMENT-BY-MOMENT POSSIBILITY WHILE WE LIVE."

MORE SHANE TRIVIA
+ TEACHING PASTOR AT MARS HILL BIBLE CHURCH IN GRAND RAPIDS, MICHIGAN, WHICH MEETS IN A FORMER SUPERMARKET
+ WORKED AS AN ADVERTISING EXECUTIVE ON ACCOUNTS LIKE GUINNESS AND PORSCHE
+ WENT TO SEMINARY AS A CALVINIST AND IS NOW A MENNONITE
+ WEARS VIBRAM FIVE FINGERS WHEN HE RUNS
+ BA FROM TEXAS CHRISTIAN UNIVERSITY
+ MDIV FROM FULLER THEOLOGICAL SEMINARY

SHANE'S BOOKS:
+ FLICKERING PIXELS: HOW TECHNOLOGY SHAPES YOUR FAITH
+ SELLING WATER BY THE RIVER: A BOOK ABOUT THE LIFE JESUS AND THE RELIGION THAT GETS IN THE WAY

QUESTIONS OF SALVATION HAVE BEEN AT THE FOREFRONT OF CHRISTIAN CONVERSATION FOR GENERATIONS. WE CONTINUE TO ASK OURSELVES BIG QUESTIONS ABOUT HOW WE ARE SAVED AND WHAT PART, IF ANY, WE PLAY IN OUR OWN SALVATION. WHAT DO YOU THINK?

IS SALVATION SOMETHING WE CAN GAIN AND LOSE?

IS SALVATION A GIFT? HOW IS IT GIVEN, RECEIVED?

SHANE HIPPS SAYS THAT WHEN JESUS WAS TALKING ABOUT ETERNAL LIFE, THE KINGDOM OF GOD, OR THE KINGDOM OF HEAVEN, HE MOST OFTEN USED THE PRESENT TENSE.

THEOLOGIANS, ARTISTS, WRITERS, AND
CHRISTIANS OF ALL STRIPES HAVE
SPENT CENTURIES TRYING TO FIGURE
OUT WHAT SALVATION IS REALLY
ABOUT. THE IDEAS THAT HAVE COME
FROM ALL THAT EFFORT ARE OFTEN
HELPFUL, BUT SOMETIMES THEY ARE
SO COMPELLING THAT THEY KEEP US
FROM EXPLORING OTHER IDEAS.

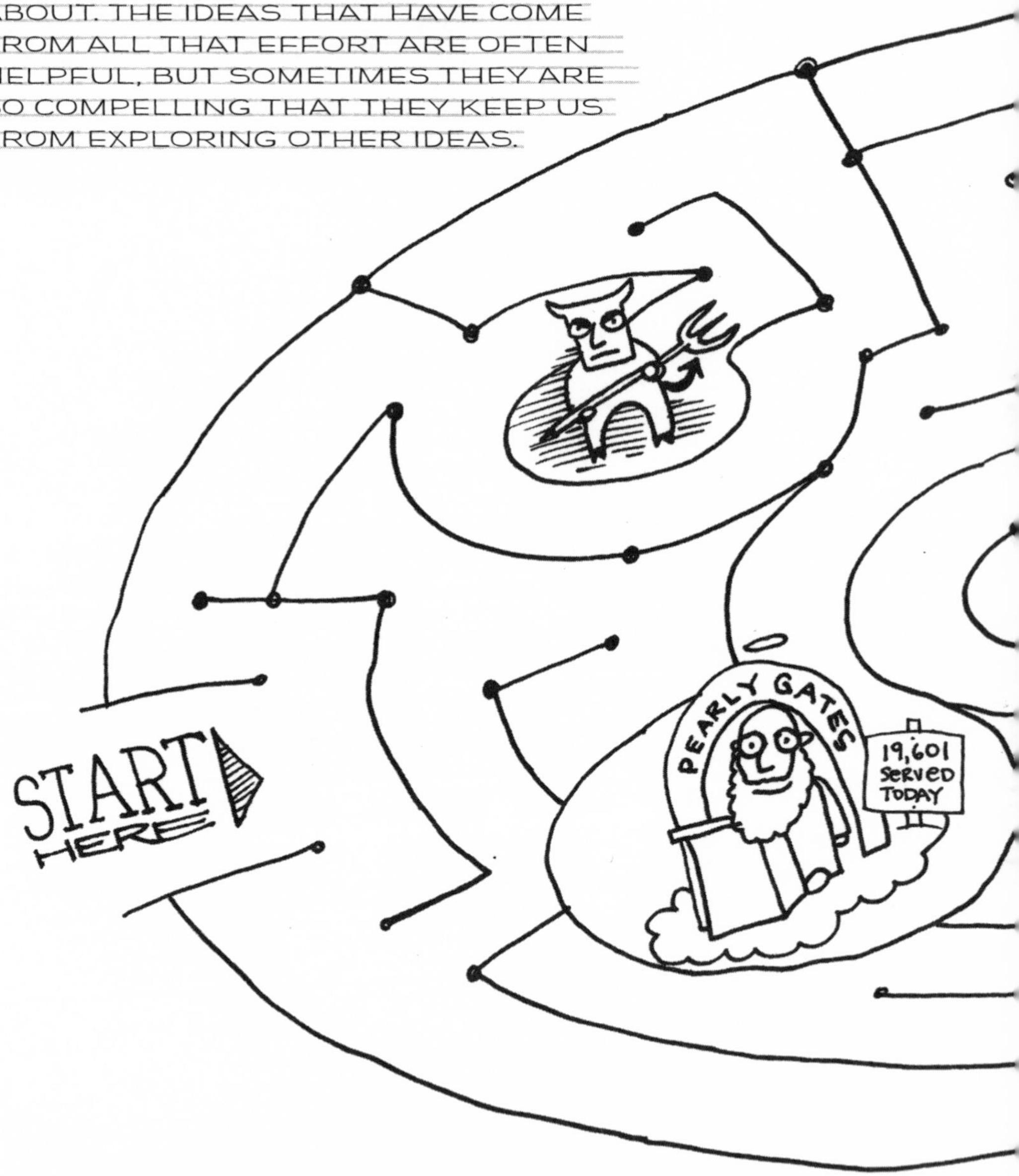

START HERE

PEARLY GATES

19,601
SERVED
TODAY

SHANE ASKS US TO MAKE OUR WAY BACK TO WHAT JESUS HAD
TO SAY ABOUT SALVATION. WHAT DO JESUS' WORDS SUGGEST?

SHANE BELIEVES THAT SALVATION HAS AT LEAST AS MUCH TO DO
WITH THIS LIFE AS THE NEXT. WHAT DO YOU THINK ABOUT THAT?

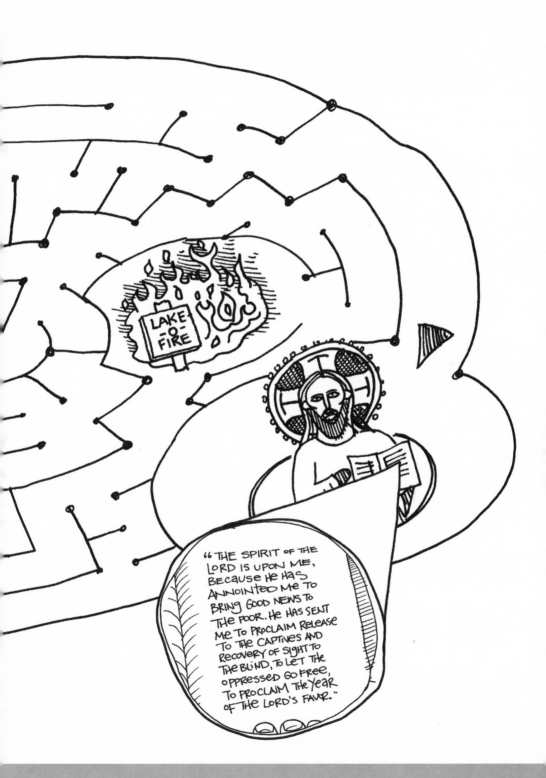

The Kingdom

THE OLD TESTAMENT TALKS ABOUT SALVATION, BUT THERE WAS NO SENSE OF AN AFTERLIFE AND NO JESUS. SO WHAT DID THEY MEAN?

EXODUS 15:2:
THE LORD IS MY STRENGTH AND MY MIGHT, AND HE HAS BECOME MY SALVATION; THIS IS MY GOD, AND I WILL PRAISE HIM, MY FATHER'S GOD, AND I WILL EXALT HIM.

2 CHRONICLES 6:41:
LET YOUR PRIESTS, O LORD GOD, BE CLOTHED WITH SALVATION, AND LET YOUR FAITHFUL REJOICE IN YOUR GOODNESS.

PSALM 27:1:
THE LORD IS MY LIGHT AND MY SALVATION; WHOM SHALL I FEAR? THE LORD IS THE STRONGHOLD OF MY LIFE; OF WHOM SHALL I BE AFRAID?

PSALM 62:5-6:
FOR GOD ALONE MY SOUL WAITS IN SILENCE, FOR MY HOPE IS FROM HIM. HE ALONE IS MY ROCK AND MY SALVATION, MY FORTRESS; I SHALL NOT BE SHAKEN.

p 20763

# of Heaven

ON EARTH · AS IT IS IN HEAVEN

THY KINGDOM COME

THY WILL·BE DONE

WHEN YOU THINK OF SALVATION, DO YOU THINK OF IT
AS BEING SAVED FROM SOMETHING OR TO SOMETHING?

HOW DOES OUR SENSE OF SALVATION INFLUENCE
THE DECISIONS WE MAKE, THE LIFE WE LIVE NOW?

IF YOU THOUGHT THIS WAS IT, WOULD YOU LIVE DIFFERENTLY?"

THE CLOCK IS TICKING. WHAT ARE YOU DOING WITH YOUR SALVATION?

3

NOTES

animate

NOTES

animate

CROSS | WHERE GOD IS
NADIA BOLZ-WEBER

NADIA BOLZ-WEBER HAS BEEN THE PASTOR
OF HOUSE FOR ALL SINNERS AND SAINTS
IN DENVER SINCE ITS INCEPTION IN 2008.
IN 2008, HER FIRST BOOK, *SALVATION ON
THE SMALL SCREEN*, DOCUMENTED HER EXPERIENCE
OF WATCHING 24 CONSECUTIVE
HOURS OF THE TRINITY BROADCAST NETWORK.

SINCE THEN, SHE HAS CONTINUED TO SPEAK,
PREACH, AND WRITE ABOUT THE DELICATE
BALANCE BETWEEN THE ANCIENT LITURGICAL
TRADITIONS OF HER DENOMINATION AND
THE POSTMODERN SENSIBILITIES OF
TODAY'S CHRISTIANS.

FOR NADIA, THE CROSS TELLS US AS MUCH ABOUT
THE NATURE OF GOD AS IT DOES ABOUT THE STATE
OF HUMANITY.

MORE NADIA TRIVIA
+ ORDAINED LUTHERAN MINISTER, ELCA
+ WORKED AS A STAND-UP COMEDIAN
+ COLLECTS BELT BUCKLES
+ BLOGS AT SARCASTICLUTHERAN.COM
+ BA IN RELIGIOUS STUDIES FROM
  UNIVERSITY OF COLORADO AT BOULDER
+ MDIV FROM THE ILIFF SCHOOL OF THEOLOGY

NADIA'S BOOKS:
+ SALVATION ON THE SMALL SCREEN

A PAIR OF NADIA'S TATTOOS READ "SIMIL IUSTUS ET PECCATOR" WHICH
MEANS "SIMULTANEOUSLY SAINT AND SINNER" IN LATIN.
CENTRAL TO NADIA'S UNDERSTANDING OF FAITH IS THIS IDEA
THAT HUMAN BEINGS ARE A MIX OF CONTRADICTIONS AND
THAT THERE IS ALWAYS SOME TENSION IN THE MIDST OF
THE STORIES WE TELL. THAT'S TRUE OF THE CROSS
AS WELL. THE CROSS HAS LONG CARRIED IT'S OWN
SEEMING CONTRADICTIONS. IT IS A SYMBOL OF
DESTRUCTION AND RENEWAL, DEATH AND LIFE,
OPPRESSION AND FREEDOM. THIS TENSION
BETWEEN DESPAIR AND HOPE IS EVERYWHERE
IN THE TWISTED ROAD OF THE CHRISTIAN STORY.

THE CROSS
HAS BEEN A
SYMBOL OF
THE CHRISTIAN
CHURCH SINCE
THE DEATH AND
RESURRECTION
OF JESUS. BUT
LIKE SO MUCH
IN THE WINDING,
TANGLED
CHRISTIAN
STORY, IT
HAS BEEN
INTERPRETED
IN VASTLY
DIFFERENT WAYS.
IT HAS BEEN
ENCRUSTED
WITH JEWELS
TO SHOW THE
WEALTH AND
POWER OF THE
CHURCH, HELD
AT THE HEAD
OF ADVANCING
ARMIES
FIGHTING IN THE
NAME OF GOD,
AND TWISTED
INTO AN ALMOST
UNRECOGNIZABLE
FORM BY THE
NAZIS. YET
EVEN WHEN
IT'S MANGLED
AND MISUSED,
IT REMAINS
A POWERFUL
SYMBOL.

AS YOU LOOK AT THESE CROSSES; WHICH ONES ARE YOU DRAWN TO? WHICH ONES FEEL WEIRD OR COMFORTING OR REPULSIVE?

IF YOU WERE TO ADD AN ADJECTIVE TO EACH OF THESE CROSSES, WHAT WOULD YOU WRITE?"

WHEN WE REALLY LOOK, WE SEE WHO GOD IS IN HOW GOD CHOSE TO REVEAL GOD'S SELF IN A CRADLE AND ON A CROSS

—NADIA BOLZ-WEBER

THE CROSS AS VICTORY OVER EVIL

WHAT DOES THE CROSS MEAN?

THERE ARE TWO BRANCHES OF THIS THEORY...

THIS IS BRANCH ONE

THE RANSOM THEORY

THIS IS BRANCH 2

CHRISTUS VICTOR

"FOR THE SON OF MAN CAME NOT TO BE SERVED BUT TO SERVE, AND TO GIVE HIS LIFE A RANSOM FOR MANY"

- MARK 10:45

RANSOM THEORY: ORIGIN (184-253)

"SINCE, THEREFORE, THE CHILDREN SHARE FLESH AND BLOOD, HE HIMSELF LIKEWISE SHARED THE SAME THINGS, SO THAT THROUGH DEATH HE MIGHT DESTROY THE ONE WHO HAS THE POWER OF DEATH, THAT IS, THE DEVIL."

- HEBREWS 2:14

CHRISTUS VICTOR: GREGORY OF NYSSA (335-395)

THE CROSS AS A MORAL LESSON

NO ONE HAS GREATER LOVE THAN THIS, TO LAY DOWN ONE'S LIFE FOR ONE'S FRIENDS.

- JOHN 15:13

JESUS IS THE PERFECT MAN, SO IN HIS DEATH, HE IS THE EXAMPLE OF GOD'S PURE SELFLESSNESS

JESUS A+

MOST FAMOUS PROPONENT: PETER ABELARD (1079-1140)

JUST AS THERE ARE MANY IMAGES OF THE CROSS, THERE HAVE BEEN MANY WAYS OF UNDERSTANDING THE CROSS OVER THE CENTURIES, EACH ONE TRYING TO ANSWER THE QUESTION "WHAT EXACTLY WAS ACCOMPLISHED ON THE CROSS?"

CROSS AS THE SATISFACTION OF GOD'S WRATH

SUBSTITUTION & ↳ ANSELM OF CANTERBURY (1033-1109)

The SCAPEGOAT
↳ RENE GIRARD (1932-PRESENT)

...T GOD PROVES HIS LOVE ...R US IN THAT WHILE WE ...TILL WERE SINNERS CHRIST ...IED FOR US. MUCH MORE SURELY THEN, NOW THAT WE HAVE BEEN JUSTIFIED BY HIS BLOOD, WILL WE BE SAVED THROUGH HIM FROM THE WRATH OF GOD. -ROMANS 5:8-9

...E HIMSELF BORE OUR SINS IN HIS BODY ON THE CROSS, SO THAT, FREE FROM SIN, WE MIGHT LIVE FOR RIGHTEOUSNESS; BY HIS WOUNDS YOU HAVE BEEN HEALED 1 PETER 2:24

The Cross AS A MEANS of Transformation

MOST FAMOUS PROPONENT: IRENAEUS (2nd CENTURY)

THROUGH THE CROSS, GOD OPENS A DOOR BY WHICH HUMANS CAN BECOME HOLY AND MORE LIKE GOD.

THUS HE HAS GIVEN US, THROUGH THESE THINGS, HIS PRECIOUS AND GREAT PROMISES, SO THAT THROUGH THEM YOU MAY ESCAPE [FROM THE CORRUPTION] THAT IS IN THE WORLD BECAUSE OF LUST, AND MAY BECOME PARTICIPANTS IN THE DIVINE NATURE -2 PETER 1:4

THE DISCUSSIONS ABOUT
THE CROSS ARE REALLY
DISCUSSIONS ABOUT THE
NATURE OF GOD. THAT'S WHY
THEY ARE DIFFICULT, EVEN
TUMULTUOUS, CONVERSATIONS
WITHIN THE CHURCH. THE
CONFLICT COMES BACK TO
THIS DICHOTOMY WE FIND IN
SO MUCH OF OUR FAITH. IS GOD
LOVING OR VENGEFUL? IS IT
POSSIBLE FOR GOD TO BE BOTH?

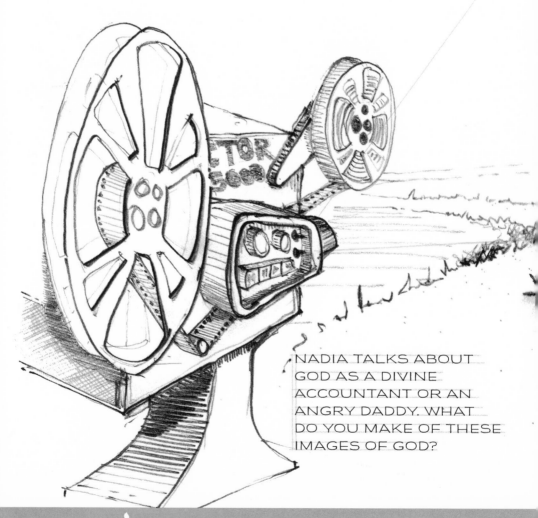

NADIA TALKS ABOUT
GOD AS A DIVINE
ACCOUNTANT OR AN
ANGRY DADDY. WHAT
DO YOU MAKE OF THESE
IMAGES OF GOD?

animate

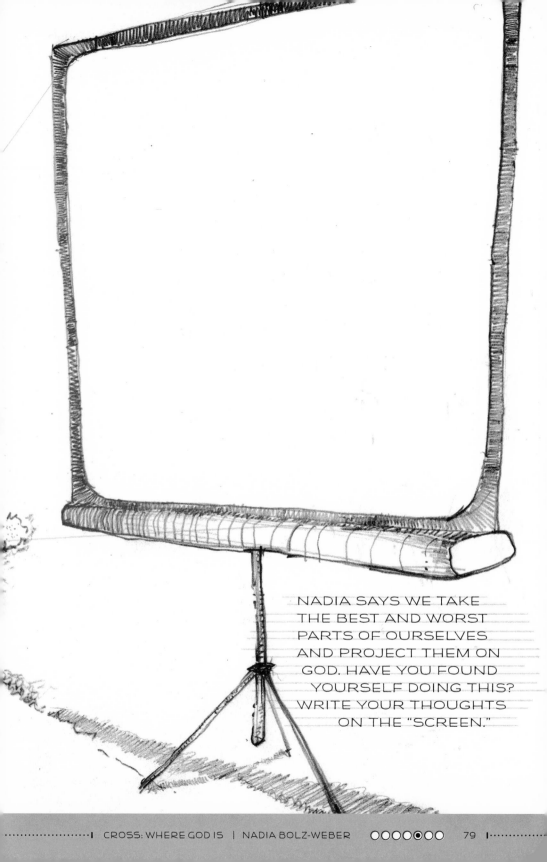

NADIA SAYS WE TAKE
THE BEST AND WORST
PARTS OF OURSELVES
AND PROJECT THEM ON
GOD. HAVE YOU FOUND
YOURSELF DOING THIS?
WRITE YOUR THOUGHTS
ON THE "SCREEN."

ADD YOUR OWN ICONS TO THE ROADSIDE SHRINE.

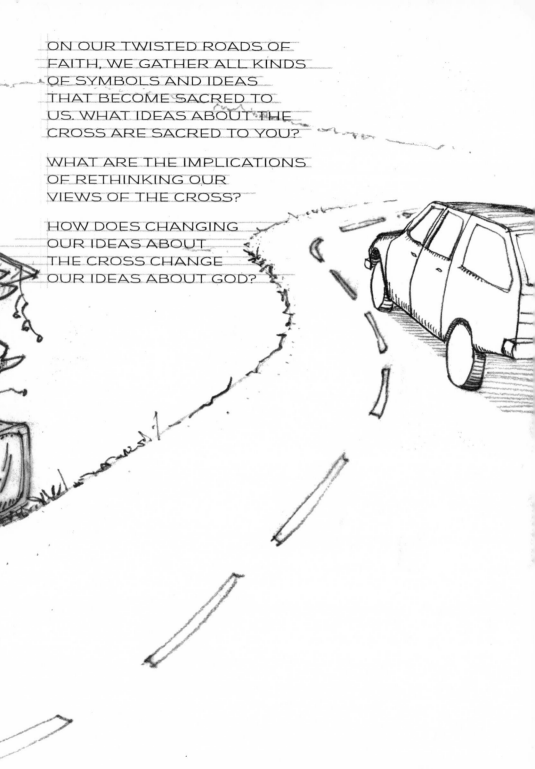

ON OUR TWISTED ROADS OF
FAITH, WE GATHER ALL KINDS
OF SYMBOLS AND IDEAS
THAT BECOME SACRED TO
US. WHAT IDEAS ABOUT THE
CROSS ARE SACRED TO YOU?

WHAT ARE THE IMPLICATIONS
OF RETHINKING OUR
VIEWS OF THE CROSS?

HOW DOES CHANGING
OUR IDEAS ABOUT
THE CROSS CHANGE
OUR IDEAS ABOUT GOD?

Notes

what makes us
choose the bedazzled
cross vs the
real cross —

2nd Corinthians.

NOTES

animate

BIBLE | A BOOK LIKE NO OTHER
LAUREN WINNER

IS THE BIBLE WORTH Re-READING

animate

HOW DO WE LIVE WITH SCRIPTURE IN A WAY THAT SHOWS THE WORDS ARE UNIQUE?

over AND over AND over?

"THE CHURCH — AND THAT'S US; WE ARE THE CHURCH — THE CHURCH HAS GROPED FOR WAYS TO TALK ABOUT THE WAYS THE BIBLE REVEALS TO US WHO WE REALLY ARE — WE HAVE GROPED FOR WAYS TO TALK ABOUT ALL THE BIBLE CAN REAVEAL TO US ABOUT GOD AND GOD'S WORLD."

-LAUREN WINNER

WHO IS LAUREN WINNER?

LAUREN BROKE ONTO THE CHRISTIAN SCENE WITH HER 2002 BOOK, *GIRL MEETS GOD*, IN WHICH SHE CHRONICLES HER CONVERSION FIRST TO ORTHODOX JUDAISM, THEN TO CHRISTIANITY. SHE IS AN ASSISTANT PROFESSOR OF CHRISTIAN SPIRITUALITY AT DUKE DIVINITY SCHOOL.

WHEN LAUREN FIRST STARTED ATTENDING WEEKLY WORSHIP SERVICES, SHE WAS STRUCK BY THE WAY THE CHURCH TREATED SCRIPTURE. SHE SAYS, "I FOUND IT STRANGE THAT WE KEPT READING THE SAME BOOK OVER AND OVER AGAIN. WEEK AFTER WEEK, YEAR AFTER YEAR, THIS ENDLESS REREADING OF THIS ONE BOOK."

LAUREN TRIVIA:

+ BA FROM COLUMBIA UNIVERSITY
+ MPHIL FROM CAMBRIDGE UNIVERSITY
+ MDIV FROM DUKE DIVINITY SCHOOL
+ PHD IN HISTORY FROM COLUMBIA
+ FELLOW AT THE INSTITUTE OF SACRED MUSIC AT YALE UNIVERSITY
+ OWNS 30 PAIRS OF CAT-EYE GLASSES
+ DOESN'T OWN A TV
+ READS. A LOT. A WHOLE LOT.
+ WROTE HER DISSERTATION ABOUT CHRISTIAN PRACTICES IN 18TH CENTURY VIRGINIA
+ DOESN'T USE SOCIAL MEDIA. AT ALL.

LAUREN'S BOOKS:

GIRL MEETS GOD
MUDHOUSE SABBATH
REAL SEX
STILL

DUKE CHAPEL

THE BIBLE IS A COLLECTION, AKA "CANON," OF 66 BOOKS BY ALMOST AS MANY AUTHORS.

ERASMUS
DUTCH HUMANIST, REFORM-
MINDED CATHOLIC PRIEST,
SCHOLAR, LINGUIST.
IN 1516 PUBLISHED GREEK
NEW TESTAMENT WHICH
HE COMPILED FROM
ANCIENT MANUSCIPTS.

"I TOLD PARSONS TO LEAVE
THEIR WRANGLINGS AND
READ THE BIBLE... I TOLD
POPES AND CARDINALS TO
LOOK AT THE APOSTLES,
AND MAKE THEMSELVES
MORE LIKE TO THEM."

DESIDERIUS
ERASMUS OF
ROTTERDAM
•1466 - 1536

THOMAS MERTON
TRAPPIST MONK, SPIRITUALIST, AUTHOR, POET

GREATEST HITS:
THE SEVEN STOREY MOUNTAIN
LIFE IN SOLITUDE
NEW SEEDS OF CONTEMPLATION

+ A COMMITTED PACIFIST, MERTON
  PROTESTED THE VIETNAM WAR.
+ LIVED AT THE ABBEY OF
  GETHSEMANI IN KENTUCKY
+ BELIEVED SPIRITUALITY IS THE
  MYSTICAL UNION BETWEEN
  A HUMAN BEING AND GOD.
  SCRIPTURE HELPS US MAKE SENSE
  OF THAT UNION, BUT IT DOESN'T
  REPLACE OR CREATE THAT UNION.

THOMAS MERTON
•1915 - 1968

" The BIBLE is ABUNDANT IN A WEIRD AND
UNIQUE WAY. I have come into that RICHER
UNDERSTANDING OF THE [BIBLE] NOT BY thinking
abstractly ABOUT IT, BUT BY ACTUALLY Living
with IT, READING it, PRAYING it,
AND praying THAT I might become A PERSON WHO
CAN Hear its LIVELINESS."
— Lauren Winner

The Holy Bible: USES & ABUSES

A SKETCHY CRYPTIC VISUAL QUASI-SURVEY

THE BIBLE HAS A STRANGE AND SOMETIMES UGLY HISTORY. IT'S BEEN USED AS A WORD OF HOPE, A WARNING SIGN, A WEAPON, AND A STATUS SYMBOL. IT'S BEEN USED TO LIBERATE AND TO OPPRESS. IT'S BEEN REVERED AND REVILED. DESPITE ALL OF THAT, WE KEEP TELLING ITS STORIES AND LOOKING TO IT FOR HELP. WHY IS THAT?

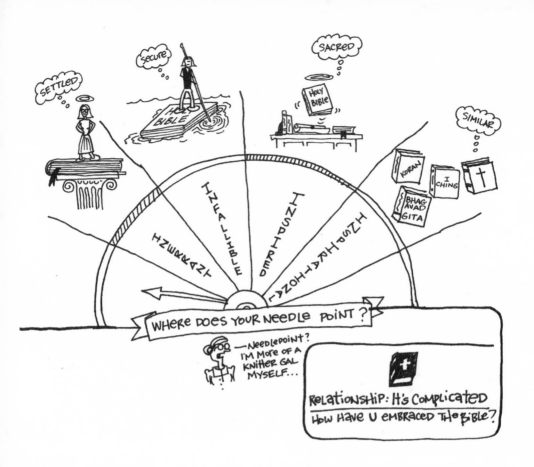

LET'S NOT JUST SIT HERE TALKING ABOUT HOW THE BIBLE IS **UNIQUE**. LET'S LIVE WITH THE WORDS OF SCRIPTURE IN A WAY THAT SHOWS THAT THOSE WORDS ARE *unique*

LAUREN'S PRACTICE OF "DISLOCATED READING" HAS HELPED HER FIND WAYS TO DISCOVER NEW MEANING IN THE WORDS OF THE BIBLE.

• HAVE YOU EVER READ THE BIBLE IN AN UNUSUAL PLACE?

• WHERE WOULD YOU NEVER BE CAUGHT DEAD READING THE BIBLE?

GO AHEAD, WRITE ON IT. WHAT VERSE OR BIT
OF THE BIBLE IS SO MEANINGFUL TO YOU THAT
YOU WOULD WANT TO INGEST IT, TO LITERALLY
TAKE IT IN AND MAKE IT PART OF
YOU? WRITE IT ON THE EGG.

(YOU DON'T HAVE TO EAT IT.)

LET THE FIELD EXULT, AND EVERYTHING IN IT!

by reading the scriptures I am so renewed that —
with me. The sky seems to be a pure, cooler blue,
"charged" with the glory of God and I

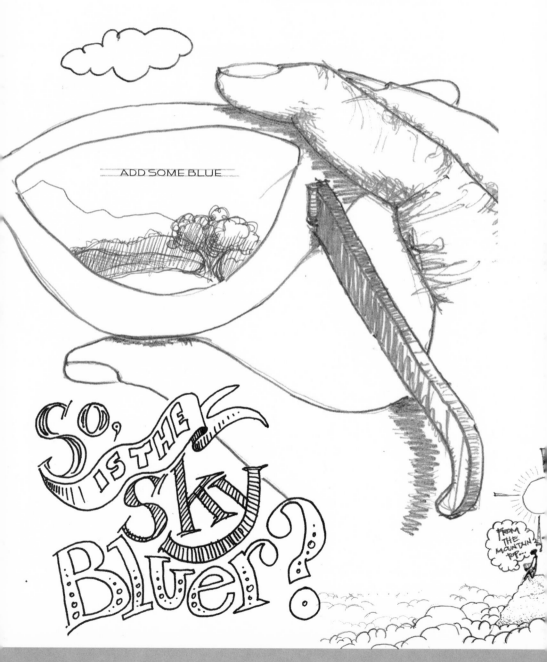

all nature seems renewed around me and the trees, a deeper green. The whole 🌎 is feel 🔥FIRE🔥 AND (MUSIC)🎸 under my FEET
—THOMAS MERTON

ADD SOME BLUE

SO, IS THE SKY BLUER?

FROM THE MOUNTAIN TOP...

NOTES

NOTES

CHURCH | AN IMPERFECT FAMILY
BRUCE REYES-CHOW

WHAT FACTORS WEIGH IN ON YOUR DECISION TO GO TO CHURCH—

WHETHER new TO YOUR CHURCH, A Longtime MEMBER — OR EVEN THE PASTOR — there are times when NOT BEING part of a church seems like the best option for expressing AND LIVING ONE'S FAITH

~ BRUCE REYES-CHOW

OR NOT? ADD THEM TO THEIR RESPECTIVE SIDE OF THE SCALE.

BRUCE CONFESSES THAT THERE ARE PLENTY OF MORNINGS WHEN HE SIMPLY DOESN'T WANT TO GO TO CHURCH. AND YET, HE GOES. FOR BRUCE, THE CHURCH, LIKE ANY FAMILY, IS A PLACE TO GROW AND BECOME WHO HE WAS MEANT TO BE.

INCREASINGLY, CHRISTIANS ARE ASKING WHAT MAKES THE CHURCH RELEVANT. WE WANT TO KNOW WHY IT'S WORTH THE TIME AND EFFORT TO BE PART OF SOMETHING THAT IS OFTEN DYSFUNCTIONAL AND EVEN HARMFUL. YET BRUCE SUGGESTS THAT BY RECLAIMING THE IDEA OF CHURCH AS FAMILY, WE CAN FIND WAYS TO EMBRACE BOTH THE PAINFUL AND THE BEAUTIFUL WAYS THAT CHURCH CHANGES US.

BRUCE TRIVIA:
+ PLANTED MISSION BAY COMMUNITY CHURCH IN SAN FRANCISCO IN 2000
+ STARTING AN ONLINE CHURCH IN 2012
+ ELECTED AND SERVED FOR TWO YEARS AS MODERATOR OF THE 218TH GENERAL ASSEMBLY OF THE PRESBYTERIAN CHURCH USA. IT'S KIND OF LIKE BEING THE POPE ONLY WITHOUT THE SNAZZY HAT.
+ SOCIAL MEDIA GURU
+ BA IN ASIAN AMERICAN STUDIES, SOCIOLOGY, AND RELIGION FROM SAN FRANCISCO STATE UNIVERSITY
+ MDIV FROM SAN FRANCISCO THEOLOGICAL SEMINARY.

WHAT **is** CHURCH?

WHAT DO EACH OF THESE FORMS SUGGEST ABOUT THE CHURCH?

EARLY CHRISTIAN HOUSE CHURCH

ORTHODOX BASILICA

CHURCH ROW

MEDIEVAL CATHEDRAL

PURITAN MEETING HOUSE

FIRST

ONE-ROOM COUNTRY CHURCH

ST.

20TH CENT. SUBURBAN CHURCH

MEGA

MODERN MEGACHURCH

CHURCH PUB

HAPPY HOUR

CHURCH-IN-A-PUB

THE ARCHITECTURE OF A CHURCH REFLECTS
THE STYLE OF THE DAY, BUT IT ALSO REFLECTS
WHAT PEOPLE THOUGHT ABOUT THE
FUNCTION OF THE CHURCH—WHO HAD THE
AUTHORITY, WHO WAS WELCOME, WHAT ROLE
THE CHURCH PLAYED IN A COMMUNITY.

WHO IS CHURCH?

BRUCE MENTIONS A HANDFUL OF
METAPHORS FOR THE CHURCH:
+ A SOCIAL CLUB
+ A CLASSROOM
+ A SPORTING EVENT
+ A THEATER
+ A HOSPITAL

WHY DO THESE STICK AROUND?

WHAT MAKES THEM WORK?

WHAT ARE THEIR LIMITS?

HOW DOES BRUCE'S METAPHOR
OF CHURCH AS FAMILY WORK?
IS IT TOO CLICHÉD?

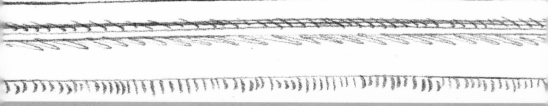

animate

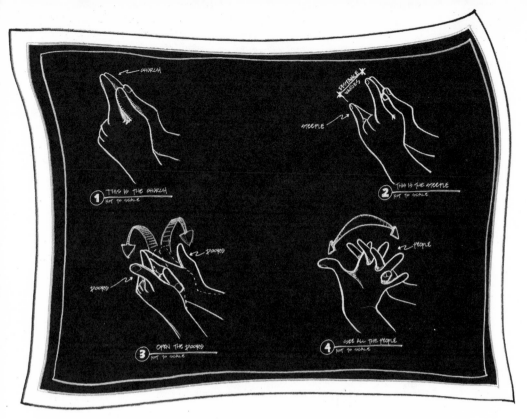

THE BIBLE OFFERS SOME METAPHORS AS WELL

+ THE BODY OF CHRIST (I CORINTHIANS 12:12-27)
+ VINE AND BRANCHES (JOHN 15:5)
+ BRIDE OF CHRIST (EPHESIANS 5:25-27)
+ WHERE TWO OR MORE ARE GATHERED (MATTHEW 18:20)
+ THE LIVING TEMPLE (EPHESIANS 2:17-22)

WHAT DO THESE TELL YOU ABOUT THE WAY EARLY CHRISTIANS THOUGHT ABOUT CHURCH?

LIKE? DRAW A FAMILY PORTRAIT IN THE FRAME.

animate

animate

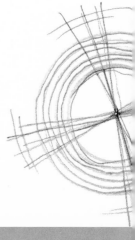

ISBN 978-1-4514-3084-4

Titus John –

Chap. 4   7-12

Romans –